Skills Builders

Grammar and Punctuation

YEAR 6

Maddy Barnes

RISING STARS

Rising Stars UK Ltd, 7 Hatchers Mews, Bermondsey Street, London SE1 3GS
www.risingstars-uk.com

Every effort has been made to trace copyright holders and obtain their permission for the use of copyright materials. The publishers will gladly receive information enabling them to rectify any error or omission in subsequent editions.

All facts are correct at time of going to press.

Published 2013
Reprinted 2013, 2014 (twice)
Text, design and layout © 2013 Rising Stars UK Ltd

Project manager: Dawn Booth
Editorial: Sue Walton
Proofreader: Margaret Crowther
Design: Words & Pictures Ltd, London
Cover design: Amina Dudhia
Acknowledgement: p.24 iStock/olegtok

British Library Cataloguing-in-Publication Data
A CIP record for this book is available from the British Library.

ISBN: 978-0-85769-697-7
Printed in Singapore by Craft Print International

Skills Builders: Grammar and Punctuation

YEAR
6

Contents

* Revision pages

How to use this book

What we have included:

1 Each unit covers aspects of grammar and punctuation taken from the new National Curriculum framework.

2 The units at the beginning of the book focus on basic skills which pupils should recognise from their previous learning and set mini challenges to encourage pupils to recap what they already know. These are often 'Warming up' questions, which are also used to test just learned knowledge throughout the book.

3 Other sections introduce new skills which are organised in a 'Getting hotter' section and some push even further in the 'Burn it up!' section.

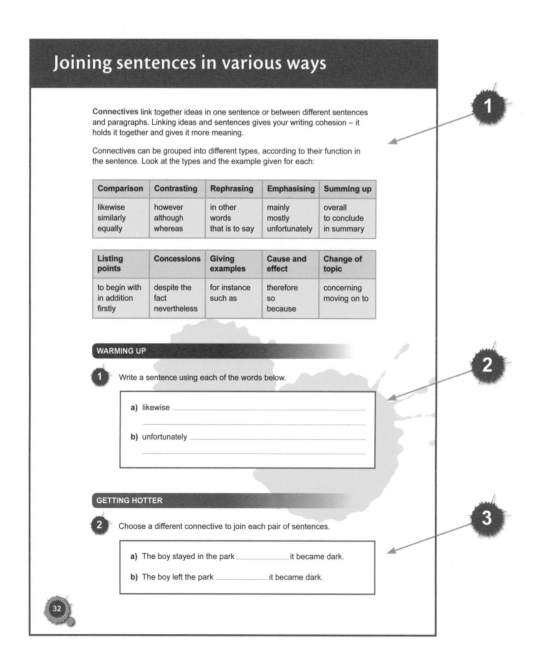

Joining sentences in various ways

Connectives link together ideas in one sentence or between different sentences and paragraphs. Linking ideas and sentences gives your writing cohesion – it holds it together and gives it more meaning.

Connectives can be grouped into different types, according to their function in the sentence. Look at the types and the example given for each:

Comparison	Contrasting	Rephrasing	Emphasising	Summing up
likewise similarly equally	however although whereas	in other words that is to say	mainly mostly unfortunately	overall to conclude in summary

Listing points	Concessions	Giving examples	Cause and effect	Change of topic
to begin with in addition firstly	despite the fact nevertheless	for instance such as	therefore so because	concerning moving on to

WARMING UP

1 Write a sentence using each of the words below.

> **a)** likewise _____
>
> _____
>
> **b)** unfortunately _____
>
> _____

GETTING HOTTER

2 Choose a different connective to join each pair of sentences.

> **a)** The boy stayed in the park _____ it became dark.
>
> **b)** The boy left the park _____ it became dark.

32

4

How to use this book

4 At the end of each section is a 'How did I do?' assessment for learning where pupils can record how well they did.

5 There are assessment points throughout the book titled 'Assess and review', which allow opportunities for pupils to recap new learning in small steps.

6 The correct grammatical terminology is used throughout this book to encourage acquisition of technical language.

7 All answers are included so pupils can check on their progress.

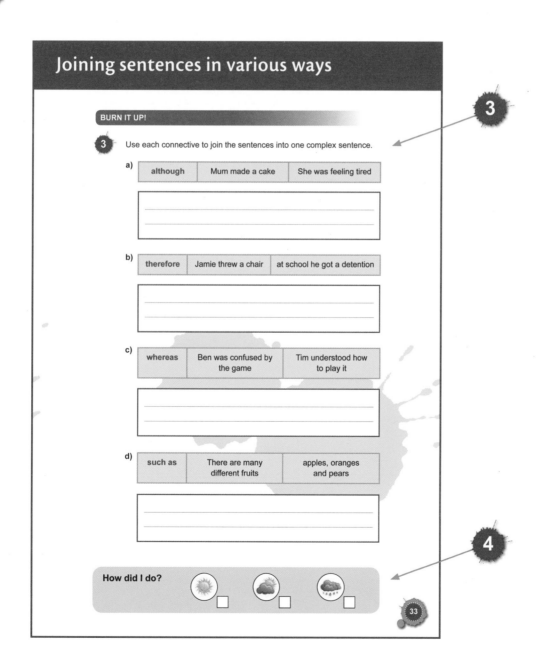

Joining sentences in various ways

BURN IT UP!

3 Use each connective to join the sentences into one complex sentence.   **3**

a)

although	Mum made a cake	She was feeling tired

b)

therefore	Jamie threw a chair	at school he got a detention

c)

whereas	Ben was confused by the game	Tim understood how to play it

d)

such as	There are many different fruits	apples, oranges and pears

How did I do?   **4**

33

Adding prefixes

A **prefix** is a group of letters placed at the start of a word. The prefix changes the meaning of the word. Here are some common prefixes:

dis-	im-	in-	mis-	re-	un-
not	not	not	wrong	again	not
disconnect	**im**possible	**in**human	**mis**behave	**re**cycle	**un**certain

WARMING UP

1 Think of three new words which start with these prefixes.

a) dis- ....

b) mis- ....

c) un- ....

GETTING HOTTER

2 Use your knowledge of prefixes to explain each of these words.

a) disadvantage ....
....

b) unavailable ....
....

c) mistake ....
....

d) unhappy ....
....

e) insane ....
....

f) immature ....
....

How did I do?

 ☐   ☐   ☐

Adding suffixes

A **suffix** is a group of letters placed at the end of a word. Knowing suffixes can make spelling easier and increases your vocabulary. Here are some common suffixes:

-ness	-ian	-able	-less	-ful	-er
friendliness	magician	comfortable	hopeless	beautiful	teacher

WARMING UP

 1 Adding the suffix **-ian** usually applies to a person. Add the suffix **-ian** to each of the following and read the new word.

a) technic........................ b) music........................

c) electric........................ d) beautic........................

e) optic........................ f) politic........................

GETTING HOTTER

 2 Add the correct suffix to these root words to make a new word. Use the table of suffixes above to help you.

a) fashion .... b) garden ....

c) care .... d) forgive ....

e) football .... f) cheer ....

g) collect .... h) hope ....

How did I do?

 ☐   ☐   ☐

Sentence types

There are different types of sentences:

Statements	I saw a big, scary dog near the post office.	.
Questions	Do you know him? Have you seen the film?	?
Exclamations	Oh dear! I cannot believe you!	!
Commands	Stop! Wait! Look out!	!

WARMING UP

1 Change these statements into questions.

a) You are going swimming. ....

b) You love eating cakes. ....

GETTING HOTTER

2 Draw lines to match each sentence to its type and put the correct punctuation at the end of the sentence

a) You know what time it is   question

b) Do you know what time it is   command

c) Answer me   statement

How did I do?

 ☐   ☐   ☐

Using modal verbs

The main modal verbs are **will**, **would**, **can**, **could**, **may**, **might**, **shall**, **should**, **must** and **ought**.

Modal verbs are important for expressing degrees of certainty.

> I **might** go swimming later on with my friends.
>
> You **should** know how to do that.
>
> We **mustn't** run in the corridors at school.

WARMING UP

 1 Underline the best modal verb to fill each gap.

a) If you do not wear a coat you _____ catch a cold.

   may   might   shall   should

b) _____ you close the window for me please?

   might   would   may   could

c) _____ we go to the cinema or stay in tonight?

   may   might   shall   should

d) He _____ to try harder in maths.

   ought   should   may   shall

How did I do?

 ☐   ☐   ☐

Adverbials of probability

We use **adverbials of probability** to show how certain we are about something. Here are some adverbials of probability:

certainly	definitely	maybe	possibly	never
often	sometimes	seldom	probably	always

Maybe and **perhaps** usually come at the beginning of the clause:

> **Perhaps** it will rain tomorrow.
>
> **Maybe** I will win the Lottery this weekend!

WARMING UP

 1 Rewrite each sentence putting the adverbial of probability in the correct place.

a) It rains in Australia (**seldom**).

_____

b) I will get a certificate this week at school (**probably**).

_____

_____

c) I will pick you up at 7:30 p.m. outside the train station (**definitely**).

_____

_____

d) I go to watch the football match on Saturdays and Sundays (**often**).

_____

_____

How did I do?   ☐   ☐   ☐

Tenses

Verbs can be written in the past, present or future tense.

The **past tense** shows that something has already happened.

The **present tense** shows that something is happening now.

The **future tense** shows that something will happen after now.

 1 Complete the table below by filling in the past tense, the present tense and the future tense.

Past tense	Present tense	Future tense
He ate his lunch.	He eats his lunch.	He will eat his lunch.
	They play football.	
We walked home from school.		We will walk home from school.
		He will do his homework.
I wrote in my diary.		
	The dogs chase the cat.	
She picked flowers for the kitchen.		

How did I do?

Assess and review

1 Replace the verb phrases in these sentences with modal verbs to show possibility.

> **a)** The train will arrive at 6 p.m.
>
> ....
>
> **b)** The weather will improve this afternoon.
>
> ....
>
> ....
>
> **c)** Your teacher will give you a certificate in assembly.
>
> ....
>
> ....
>
> **d)** The dog will come home when she is hungry.
>
> ....

2 Draw lines to match each sentence type to the correct sentence and add the correct punctuation.

> **a)** Answer me   statement
>
> **b)** Did you say something   command
>
> **c)** I have already told you   question

Assess and review

3 Correct the verbs in these sentences.

a) The girls was playing in the garden.

....

b) He was jumped on the trampoline.

....

c) Yesterday I eated spaghetti for my lunch.

....

d) I will looking for my school bag tomorrow.

....

4 Write five more words using each of the suffixes **-ful** and **-cian**.

-cian	-ful
beautician	forgetful

Sentences and clauses

Phrase	A group of words that may have nouns or verbs but does not have a subject doing a verb.	some funny people running up the street
Clause	A group of words that has a subject doing a verb.	Eleanor likes dancing he paints a picture
Independent clause	A complete sentence by itself.	Ben went swimming Thomas eats doughnuts
Subordinate clause	Starts with a subordinating conjunction and does not make sense by itself.	because Eleanor likes dancing
Relative clause	Adds extra information to the sentence by modifying or defining the noun.	The car, **which was very expensive**, was shiny and red.

WARMING UP

 1   Underline the subordinate clauses in these sentences.

a) After Pam sneezed on the cake, she threw it in the bin.

b) Unless Thomas finishes his homework, he will have a detention tomorrow.

c) The dog chewed on the slipper, whilst Dad slept in his chair.

d) Although I was scared, I opened the old wooden door.

e) We will win the match, if we play our best.

f) Daniel put his hood up, because it was raining.

How did I do?   ☐   ☐   ☐

14

Direct speech

Direct speech is the exact words used by the speaker or writer. You need to put speech marks or inverted commas around what the speaker says.

> 'I can't believe I am in Year 6,' said Gabrielle to Chloe.

1 Tick the sentence that is punctuated correctly.

a) 'Stop it,' he said, 'you are hurting my leg!'	
b) 'Stop it, he said, you are hurting my leg!'	
c) Stop it!, he said, 'you are hurting my leg!'	
d) 'Stop it' he said, 'you are hurting my leg!'	

GETTING HOTTER

2 Rewrite these sentences as direct speech. Make sure you use the correct punctuation.

a) She told Aaliyah to go and get her book bag.

....

....

b) He told Dad that he had spent all of his pocket money.

....

....

c) Sally told Ellie that she had borrowed her pen.

....

....

How did I do?

15

Using brackets, commas and dashes

Brackets are sometimes called **parentheses** and the information in brackets is called **parenthesis**. Brackets show information which is extra to the main text.

Parenthesis can be written in brackets, between commas or between dashes.

> Alex King (who was the top goal scorer) played for Accrington FC.
>
> Alex King, who was the top goal scorer, played for Accrington FC.
>
> Alex King – who was the top goal scorer – played for Accrington FC.

WARMING UP

 1 Add parenthetical brackets, dashes or commas to these sentences.

a) The fashion show which starts at 6 p.m. should be an amazing night.

b) The puppies which were nearly six months old were ready to be sold.

c) The website which had a section about sport had a picture of the school football team.

d) The car which is a brand new Porsche is shiny, fast and beautiful.

How did I do?

 ☐   ☐   ☐

Apostrophe for possession and contraction

Apostrophes can be used to indicate **possession** or to show **contraction**.

Possession: This means that an apostrophe can be used to show who or what something belongs to, for example 'the boy's ball'.

Contraction: Sometimes we shorten words. When we do this we use an apostrophe to show where letters have been missed out, for example can't and won't.

WARMING UP

 1 Write the contraction for the underlined words.

> **a)** I think <u>I will</u> go to the party. ....
>
> **b)** <u>Let us</u> see what time the shop closes. ....
>
> **c)** I <u>do not</u> think I will have enough money. ....
>
> **d)** <u>I have</u> finally finished my homework! ....
>
> **e)** I cannot believe <u>they have</u> not arrived yet. ....
>
> **f)** He was so angry he <u>could not</u> speak. ....

GETTING HOTTER

 2 Rewrite these sentences inserting the apostrophe to show possession in the correct place.

> **a)** All of the girls coats had fallen onto the floor.
> ....
>
> **b)** The boys bike was resting against the apple tree.
> ....
>
> **c)** You could see two eggs in the birds nest.
> ....
>
> **d)** The mans car needed a new engine.
> ....
>
> **e)** The childrens lunch boxes were stacked up near the door.
> ....

How did I do?   ☐   ☐   ☐

Double negatives

Double negatives are not Standard English. Here are some examples of double negatives:

> **You don't know nothing** = You don't know anything.
>
> You know nothing.
>
> **I ain't got none** = I haven't got any.

WARMING UP

 1 Correct the grammar of the sentences below.

a) 'I don't know nothing about what happened!' she screamed.

....

....

b) 'I can't do no more to help you,' he shouted.

....

....

c) The girl can't buy no sweets.

....

....

How did I do?

 ☐   ☐   ☐

Informal and formal writing

Formal and informal styles must be chosen to suit the purpose of the writing.

> **Informal writing** is personal and chatty.
>
> **Formal writing** is impersonal and uses the third person.

WARMING UP

 1 Write **F** or **I** to show which sentences are formal and which are informal.

a) See ya tomorrow! ....

b) Frankly, there are too many problems to list. ....

c) That was way too cool! ....

d) Smoking is prohibited in this restaurant. ....

e) There appears to have been a misunderstanding in this conversation. ....

f) I guess I know the answer. ....

g) You know what I mean mate. ....

h) There is very little availability for the concert. ....

GETTING HOTTER

 2 Circle the more formal sentence.

a) I have saved my weekly pocket money so I'm allowed to go and spend it.

b) I've saved loads of money so I'm gonna spend it all today.

How did I do?

 ☐   ☐   ☐

Assess and review

 1 Underline the subordinate clause in these sentences.

a) Before she knew it, the cat climbed on the chair.

b) Even though she was seven, her Mum carried her up to bed every night.

c) After all the noise, the children went to sleep.

d) Now that he was in Year 6, Anthony walked home by himself.

 2 Read the sentences below and write **I** if the text in **red** is an independent clause or **S** if it is a subordinate clause.

a) **Ed took a nap** before he left to visit his friends.

b) **I am going to the party**, even though I am not planning on staying long.

c) **Although you may disagree**, this is the best book in the world.

d) They would get on much better **if they could just see eye to eye**.

 3 Rewrite what Ed and Terry said as direct speech:

> Ed asked Terry what he would like to do for his birthday. Terry replied that he would like to go to the cinema or for a meal at the new Polish restaurant. Ed tells Terry that he also wants to try the new restaurant and promises to book a table for 9 p.m. on Friday.

Assess and review

4 Edit and rewrite this text into Standard English.

Anthony: What was you doing in the playground?

Blerti: We wasn't doing nothing, just standing around. Where were you Anthony?

Anthony: I looked in the PE cupboard but there isn't no football.

....

....

....

....

....

5 Write the expanded form for each of these contractions.

couldn't   could not

a) don't   ....

b) would've   ....

c) won't   ....

d) didn't   ....

e) shouldn't   ....

How did I do?

 ☐   ☐   ☐

Word classes

Different words do different jobs in a sentence. These are called **word classes**.

Nouns can be separated into different categories:

Proper nouns	Names of people, places, times, occasions and events.	**Claire** and **James** got married in **Poland**.
Common nouns	Names of things that there are many of: animals, plants, objects.	He put the **plates** on the **table** near the **window**.
Collective nouns	Names given for groups of people, animals or other collections.	a **swarm** of bees a **flock** of sheep a **choir** of singers
Abstract nouns	Names of things you cannot see, usually feelings.	hate happiness truth

WARMING UP

1   Label each of the nouns below as either a collective noun (**CL**), a common noun (**CM**), a proper noun (**PR**), or an abstract noun (**AB**).

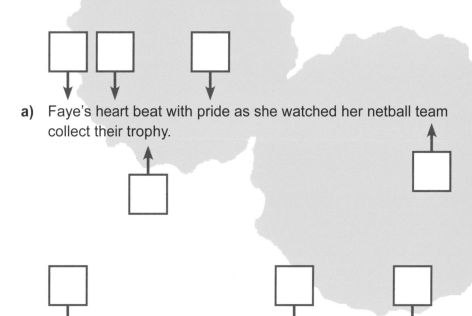

a)   Faye's heart beat with pride as she watched her netball team collect their trophy.

b)   Baljit (who was supposed to avoid stress) missed the train to Birmingham because her family were running late.

Word classes

Adjectives	Tell you more about the noun.	the **huge**, **scary** dragon the **kind**, **helpful** nurse
Pronouns	Stand in place of a noun.	**He** played on **his** bike. **That** is the best picture.
Verbs	Tell you what is happening in a sentence.	She **baked** a cake. They **are going** to school. I **will finish** it tomorrow.
Adverbs	Fill in the background detail about what happens.	I stroked the cat **gently**. He won the race **yesterday**. There are children **everywhere**.
Prepositions	Show the position of things.	She put it **under** the table. **After** lunch we went home. The cat was playing **in** the garden.

GETTING HOTTER

2 Write a pronoun to replace each underlined noun phrase.

> **a)** <u>The boys</u> had collected the boys' coats.
>
> ....
>
> **b)** <u>The girl</u> was making a cake.
>
> ....
>
> **c)** <u>The boy</u> scored a try in rugby.
>
> ....
>
> **d)** <u>The dogs</u> chased the rabbit around the garden.
>
> ....

BURN IT UP!

3 Circle the prepositions in these sentences.

a) He played outside the house.

b) Before we had our tea, we washed our hands.

c) She put the vase on top of the TV.

d) The little girl sat between the cat and the dog.

How did I do?

 ☐   ☐   ☐

23

Subject, object, verb and articles

To understand sentences you need to be able to identify the main parts. These are the **subject**, **object** and **verb**.

The dog barked.

subject   verb

The dog chased the cat.

subject   verb   object

WARMING UP

1 Underline the object in these sentences.

a) The girls sat on the benches.

b) The cat sat on the sofa.

c) The man cleaned the windows.

d) The children played in the field.

e) Paul ate a pizza for lunch.

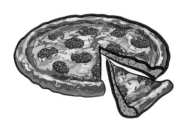

GETTING HOTTER

2 Complete the table.

Sentence	Subject	Object	Verb
The boy ran through the forest.			
The birds flew over the houses.			
The seeds were planted by the man.			
Louisa phoned her Mum after tea.			

Subject, object, verb and articles

Articles are the words **the**, **a** or **an**, which come before nouns.

The refers to a particular noun:

> **The** girl cried. **The** bird flew.

A or **an** refer to any noun:

> **A** girl cried. **A** bird flew.

An is used before nouns that start with a vowel sound:

> **an** apple, **an** umbrella, **an** octopus (but **a** euro).

BURN IT UP!

3 Write articles in the gaps in the paragraph below.

> Recently at _____ safari park I saw many different types of animal.
> My favourites were _____ penguins but I spotted _____ iguana
> hidden in the Reptile House. All in all I had _____ amazing time.

4 Write the subject noun phrase underneath each sentence.

> **a)** The bright green car skidded at the traffic lights.
>
> ....
>
> **b)** The Siamese kitten lay in front of the fire.
>
> ....
>
> **c)** After school, the Year 6 girls went to the shop.
>
> ....
>
> **d)** The house plant grew out of the pot and needed to be trimmed.
>
> ....
>
> ....

How did I do?   ☐   ☐   ☐

Using the active and passive voice

A sentence is **active** when the subject is doing the action (verb). For example:

The girl was chasing the dog.

subject   **verb**   **object**

the girl is doing
the chasing

A sentence is **passive** when the subject has the action done to it. For example:

The dog was being chased by the girl.

subject   **verb**   **object**

the dog is being
chased

WARMING UP

 Write **A** if the sentence is written in the active form and **P** if it is written in the passive form.

a) The boy was reading a book. ....

b) The question was answered by the teacher. ....

c) The footballer scored the winning goal. ....

d) The man was arrested by the policeman. ....

e) The fly was squashed by the chef. ....

f) The winning goal was scored by the footballer. ....

g) The policeman arrested the man. ....

h) The teacher answered the question. ....

Using the active and passive voice

2 Rewrite these sentences in the **active** form.

a) The winning song was sung by the boy band.

....

b) The delicious apple pie was baked by Grandma.

....

c) The phone call was answered swiftly by the emergency services.

....

....

d) The stolen car was driven by a teenage girl.

....

BURN IT UP!

3 Rewrite these sentences in the **passive** form.

a) The bird carefully built the nest.

....

b) The blue team beat the world motor racing record.

....

c) The toddler ripped the book in half.

....

d) The teacher marked the literacy books.

....

How did I do?   ☐   ☐   ☐

Comparative and superlative

The **comparative** compares two things and usually ends in **-er** or uses the word **more**.

> The girl is **shorter** than the boy.
> The chair is **more** comfortable than the floor.

The **superlative** compares three or more things and usually ends in **-est** or uses the word **most**.

> Gabrielle is loud, Chloe is louder, but Destine is the loud**est**.
> The shark is the **most** frightening creature at the zoo.

WARMING UP

 1 Some adjectives are irregular and do not follow the rules above.

Complete the table to show the comparative and superlative adjective forms.

Adjective	Comparative	Superlative
tall	taller	tallest
happy		
good		
big		
bad		
little		
busy		
many		
narrow		

How did I do?

 ☐   ☐   ☐

Identifying expanded noun phrases

Thomas **cleaned** the car.

proper noun   noun phrase

We can add detail to this sentence by expanding the noun phrase with adjectives or by adding a **prepositional phrase** or **adverbial**.

Adding adjectives = Thomas cleaned **the dirty blue car**.

Adding a prepositional phrase = Thomas cleaned **the dirty blue car in the garden**.

Adding an adverbial = **Yesterday**, Thomas cleaned **the dirty blue car in the garden**.

WARMING UP

1 Underline the expanded noun phrase in these sentences.

> **a)** I saw the old green car near the house.
>
> **b)** She was wearing a bright green dress.
>
> **c)** The cute Siamese kitten sat near the tree.
>
> **d)** I bought a wooden table with a glass top.
>
> **e)** Her garden was full of blooming, beautiful flowers.

GETTING HOTTER

2 Add an expanded noun phrase to complete these sentences.

> **a)** Sarah got off the bus and ran towards _____
>
> **b)** James threw the ball over the _____

How did I do?

 ☐   ☐   ☐

Using question tags

A **question tag** is a phrase added to the main part of the sentence, inviting the listener to confirm or give an opinion about the comment. For example:

> It isn't very warm today, **is it**?
> You have already seen this film, **haven't you**?
> He will come today, **won't he**?
> You go to school, **don't you**?

 1 Circle the question tags in the following sentences.

> **a)** You gave the secretary your dinner money, didn't you?
>
> **b)** He has the key to the house, hasn't he?
>
> **c)** You want a drink now, don't you?
>
> **d)** She has brown hair, hasn't she?

 2 Add a question tag to the following sentences.

> **a)** We can go to town later, _____ ?
>
> **b)** He will give you the ticket tomorrow, _____ ?
>
> **c)** It is really cold today, _____ ?
>
> **d)** I will have to have my eyes tested, _____ ?
>
> **e)** The party was amazing, _____ ?
>
> **f)** We should clean this room, _____ ?
>
> **g)** The dog is very scary, _____ ?
>
> **h)** They played really well, _____ ?

How did I do? ☐   ☐   ☐

Identifying verb and prepositional phrases

A **phrase** is a group of words that may have nouns and verbs but does not have a subject doing a verb. For example:

> running down the road
> some young girls
> after lunch

WARMING UP

 1 Underline all parts of the verb phrase in these sentences.

> **a)** The boys had played football for two hours.
>
> **b)** The girls were swimming in the pool all day.
>
> **c)** The children had been reading since lunch time.
>
> **d)** The babies were crying in their prams.

GETTING HOTTER

 2 Circle the prepositional phrases in these sentences.

> **a)** He left his shopping at the foot of the stairs.
>
> **b)** Grandma came into the room and closed the window.
>
> **c)** When my shopping arrived, I put the biscuits in the tin.
>
> **d)** I got a beautiful necklace for my birthday from my parents.
>
> **e)** He couldn't find the football in the weedy, overgrown garden.
>
> **f)** The baby looked warm and cosy under the soft blanket.

How did I do?   ☐   ☐   ☐

31

Joining sentences in various ways

Connectives link together ideas in one sentence or between different sentences and paragraphs. Linking ideas and sentences gives your writing cohesion – it holds it together and gives it more meaning.

Connectives can be grouped into different types, according to their function in the sentence. Look at the types and the example given for each:

Comparison	Contrasting	Rephrasing	Emphasising	Summing up
likewise similarly equally	however although whereas	in other words that is to say	mainly mostly unfortunately	overall to conclude in summary

Listing points	Concessions	Giving examples	Cause and effect	Change of topic
to begin with in addition firstly	despite the fact nevertheless	for instance such as	therefore so because	concerning moving on to

WARMING UP

 1 Write a sentence using each of the words below.

> **a)** likewise _____
>
> _____
>
> **b)** unfortunately _____
>
> _____

GETTING HOTTER

 2 Choose a different connective to join each pair of sentences.

> **a)** The boy stayed in the park _____ it became dark.
>
> **b)** The boy left the park _____ it became dark.

Joining sentences in various ways

3 Use each connective to join the sentences into one complex sentence.

a)

although	Mum made a cake	She was feeling tired

b)

therefore	Jamie threw a chair	at school he got a detention

c)

whereas	Ben was confused by the game	Tim understood how to play it

d)

such as	There are many different fruits	apples, oranges and pears

How did I do?

Conjunctions and connectives

➤ **Connectives** are words or phrases that link ideas together. Connectives can also be conjunctions.

➤ **Conjunctions** have the job of joining two ideas in a sentence, whereas other connectives join the ideas in one sentence to the ideas in another sentence or paragraph.

Some common conjunctions are: **and**, **but**, **so**, **if**, **when**, **after**, **before**, **although**.

WARMING UP

 1 Choose a conjunction from the examples above to join each pair of simple sentences.

> **a)** I want to go swimming .... it is too late.
>
> **b)** I will meet you after school .... we can do our homework.
>
> **c)** There are no biscuits left .... I will buy some more.

GETTING HOTTER

 2 Which conjunction could be used to complete these sentences? Circle one.

> **a)** Mum wanted a cup of tea .... there was no milk.
>
>   **after**   **before**   **although**
>
> **b)** The dog chased the ball .... hid it under his blanket.
>
>   **if**   **and**   **until**

Conjunctions and connectives

 3 Tick the best ending to complete these sentences.

a) The boy stayed at school until

he had not finished playing football.	
he could not have a biscuit.	
he had finished playing football.	
his Dad thought it was Wednesday.	

b) Tilly managed to get to the football match even though

she had already got a ticket on time.	
she didn't forget her ticket.	
she had originally forgotten her ticket.	
she could buy a ticket there.	

c) She was determined to go to the party although

she had not got no invitation.	
she had going to be invited.	
she had not been invited.	
she was not going to be invited.	

d) They will win the football tournament if

he scoring this penalty.	
he won't score this penalty.	
he is scoring this penalty.	
he scores this penalty.	

How did I do?   ☐   ☐   ☐

Using the colon accurately

A **colon** can be used in different ways:

To introduce a list, an example or a quotation.	:	To separate two independent clauses where the second clause expands on or illustrates the first.

However, the colon must always be preceded by a full sentence:

> **There were many precious items in the treasure chest:** gold, rubies, pearls and crystals.
>
> **The treasure chest was precious:** full of gold and other expensive jewels.

WARMING UP

 1   Complete the second part of each sentence below.

a) There were many things crowding the street:

_____

_____

_____

b) The street was extremely crowded:

_____

_____

_____

_____

Using the colon accurately

 2 Colour the sentence halves which match.

The bike was very popular:	she worked carefully and completed all of her work on time.
The ice-cream sundae was amazing:	some days it is sunny and other days it rains.
Pritika tried her best every day:	it had five gears and enhanced steering.
The weather in England varies:	decorated with chocolate sprinkles, wafers and raspberry sauce.

BURN IT UP!

 3 Complete these sentences, making sure there is a complete sentence before the colon and a complete sentence or a list after the colon.

a) The shopping bag was full of items: ....

....

b) .... : she planted

daisies, daffodils, roses and tulips.

c) Babies need to be cared for in different ways: ....

....

d) .... : he enjoyed

football, tennis and rugby.

How did I do?   ☐   ☐   ☐

Punctuation of bullet points

Bullet points are used to draw attention to important information within a document so that a reader can identify the key issues and facts quickly. There are two types of bulleted lists, **ordered** and **unordered**.

An **ordered** list means that the list is numbered:

1.
2.
3.

An **unordered** list means the list is not numbered:

●
●
●

When you are punctuating bullet points, you should use semicolons at the end of each bullet and a full stop at the end of the list. Alternatively, you can use a full stop at the end of each bullet and start each one with a capital letter.

WARMING UP

 1 Punctuate these bullet points, using both methods explained above.

a) Before you cross the road, remember to:

look left
look right
look left again
cross the road safely

b) Every time you do a piece of work you should:

write the title
write the date
underline your headings

How did I do?

 ☐   ☐   ☐

How hyphens can be used

Hyphens are short dashes between two words. For example: father-in-law.

Hyphens are used for	Examples
Some compound nouns	well-dressed, hang-glider
Verbs made from two nouns	to ice-skate,
Adding a prefix to some words	re-examine, ex-wife

WARMING UP

 1 Write definitions for these hyphenated words.

> **a)** baby-faced ....
>
> **b)** tight-fisted ....
>
> **c)** ill-tempered ....
>
> **d)** back-to-back ....
>
> **e)** action-packed ....

GETTING HOTTER

2 Write a sentence using each of these compound adjectives.

> **a)** sugar-free ....
>
> ....
>
> **b)** accident-prone ....
>
> ....

How did I do? ☐ ☐ ☐

Using a semicolon

A **semicolon** is used to separate two complete sentences that are very closely related but should not be joined with a colon. For example:

> Call me tomorrow; I will give you my answer.

There needs to be a complete sentence both before and after the semicolon, but don't use a capital letter for the second sentence.

WARMING UP

 1 Match the first half of each sentence to the most appropriate second half.

a) The moon is full;	a dark figure appeared.
b) The door swung open;	you may get dehydrated.
c) Luke's birthday is in February;	the stars are out.
d) Drink plenty of water on the journey;	Pam's is in November.

GETTING HOTTER

 2 Complete these sentences, making sure that there is a complete sentence after the semicolon.

a) Laura loved musicals; ....

b) It had rained all day; ....

c) The new shopping centre was very busy; ....

....

d) There are many different sports for children to play; ....

....

How did I do?

 ☐ ☐ ☐

Changing verbs into nouns

You can change verbs to nouns by adding **-tion**, **-ism**, **-ness**, **-ist**, **-er** and **-ity**.

For example:

Verb: to be responsible ➡ **noun: responsibility**

Verb: to be kind ➡ **noun: kindness**

 1 Change the following verbs to nouns.

Verb	Noun
to apologise	
to tour	
to dance	
to reduce	
to operate	
to be happy	
to concentrate	
to educate	
to teach	
to locate	
to satisfy	
to demonstrate	
to inform	
to decide	

How did I do?

 ☐   ☐   ☐

Recap of word classes

 1 Read each sentence and decide which word class the underlined word belongs to. Tick one box.

a) Mark looked forward to going snowboarding on <u>Friday</u>.

noun	
verb	
connective	
adjective	

b) Aoiffe saw <u>an</u> elephant washing herself at the zoo.

pronoun	
article	
preposition	
connective	

c) The children thought the <u>old</u> house looked haunted.

article	
adverb	
connective	
adjective	

d) 'Let's go for a <u>walk</u> Rob,' suggested Baljit.

verb	
adverb	
noun	
connective	

e) Angela didn't do her homework; <u>therefore</u> she got a detention.

noun	
verb	
connective	
adverb	

f) The <u>teams</u> warmed up on the pitch before the game began.

adverb	
adjective	
noun	
pronoun	

g) The teacher thought <u>her</u> pupils were amazing.

noun	
preposition	
connective	
pronoun	

h) I asked him to watch the film, but he has <u>already</u> seen it.

adjective	
adverb	
connective	
preposition	

How did I do?

 ☐   ☐   ☐

Assess and review

 1 Draw lines to match each sentence to its correct descriptions.

a) She put on her coat and left.

b) The room was cleaned by the caretaker.

c) It is our responsibility to ensure the playground is a safe place.

d) It rained like cats and dogs all day.

Informal
Formal
Active
Passive

 2 Use comparatives (ending in **-er**) or superlatives (ending in **-est**) adjectives to complete these sentences.

a) 'I don't want my hair to be cut any _____ ,' cried Eleanor.

b) 'I can't reach the top shelf, I wish I was _____ ,' said Jackie.

c) 'I am so rich, I am the _____ boy in my class,' exclaimed Dylan.

d) 'You cannot have all of the sweets; you are the _____ boy I know,' said Mrs Green.

e) 'I hate being tall, I wish I was _____ ,' moaned Claudia.

f) 'My new teacher is really mean; my old teacher was much _____ ,' said Freddie.

g) 'It is really dark in here; if you turn the light on it will be _____ ,' remarked Samuel.

Assess and review

 3   Draw lines to match the question tags and the questions.

a) He spent all of his money quickly,
b) She will pick us up later,
c) It's really dark in here

isn't it?
didn't he?
won't she?

4   Rewrite these passive sentences as active ones.

a) The bins were collected by the council on Wednesday.

_____

_____

b) The traffic was directed by the police.

_____

_____

c) The car was bought by Mrs Smith.

_____

_____

d) The pizza was eaten by the children.

_____

_____

Assess and review

We can create expanded noun phrases by adding words before and after the noun (you could try and use adjectives and prepositions).

> **the bike**
>
> **the shiny red bike leaning against the shed**

BURN IT UP!

 5 Create expanded noun phrases for the following nouns.

a) the tree

b) the rabbit

c) the teacher

d) the hat

e) the bus

How did I do?

 ☐   ☐   ☐

Answers

CUT HERE

Adding prefixes (page 6)

1 Answers will vary
   a) disappear, disapprove, disobedient, disagree
   b) mistake, misunderstood, misfortune
   c) unreasonable, unforgettable, ungrateful
2 a) not an advantage b) not available c) wrong answer / choice
   d) not happy e) not sane f) not mature

Adding suffixes (page 7)

1 a) technician b) musician c) electrician d) beautician
   e) optician f) politician
2 a) fashionable b) gardener c) careful / careless d) forgiveness
   e) footballer f) cheerful / cheerless g) collectable h) hopeful / hopeless

Sentence types (page 8)

1 a) Are you going swimming? b) Do you love eating cakes?
2 a) statement: You know what time it is.
   b) question: Do you know what time it is?
   c) command: Answer me!

Using modal verbs (page 9)

1 a) might / may b) could / would c) should / shall d) ought

Adverbials of probability (page 10)

1 a) It seldom rains in Australia.
   b) I will probably get a certificate this week at school.
   c) I will definitely pick you up at 7:30 p.m. outside the train station.
   d) I often go to watch the football match on Saturdays and Sundays.

Tenses (page 11)

1

Past tense	Present tense	Future tense
They played football.	They play football.	They will play football.
We walked home from school.	We walk home from school.	We will walk home from school.
He did his homework.	He does his homework.	He will do his homework.
I wrote in my diary.	I write in my diary.	You will write in your diary.
The dogs chased the cat.	The dogs chase the cat.	The dogs will chase the cat.
She picked flowers for the kitchen.	She picks flowers for the kitchen.	She will pick flowers for the kitchen.

For present tense also accept 'is eating', etc.

Assess and review (pages 12–13)

1 a) The train may / could / might arrive at 6 p.m.
   b) The weather might / could / should improve this afternoon.
   c) Your teacher might / could give you a certificate in assembly.
   d) The dog should / might come home when she is hungry.
2 a) command: Answer me! b) question: Did you say something?
   c) statement: I have already told you.
3 a) were b) jumping c) ate d) look
4 Answers will vary
   -cian: musician, optician, dietician, politician, electrician
   -ful: mindful, hopeful, careful, grateful, restful

Sentences and clauses (page 14)

1 a) After Pam sneezed on the cake b) Unless Thomas finishes his homework
   c) whilst Dad slept in his chair d) Although I was scared,
   e) if we play our best f) because it was raining

Direct speech (page 15)

1 a) ticked
2 a) 'Go and get your book bag Aaliyah.' b) 'I have spent all of my pocket money Dad.' c) 'I have borrowed your pen Ellie.'
   Also accept answers that include speaker details

Using brackets, commas and dashes (page 16)

1 Answers will vary. Accept pairs of dashes or commas instead of brackets.
   a) The fashion show (which starts at 6 p.m.) should be an amazing night.
   b) The puppies (which were nearly six months old) were ready to be sold.
   c) The website (which had a section about sport) had a picture of the school football team.
   d) The car (which is a brand new Porsche) is shiny, fast and beautiful.

Apostrophe for possession and contraction (page 17)

1 a) I'll b) Let's c) don't d) I've e) they've f) couldn't
2 a) girls' b) boy's c) bird's d) man's e) children's

Double negatives (page 18)

1 a) 'I don't know anything about what happened!' she screamed.
   b) 'I can't do any more to help you,' he shouted.
   c) The girl can't buy any sweets.

Informal and formal writing (page 19)

1 a) I b) F c) I d) F e) F f) I g) I h) F
2 a) I have saved my weekly pocket money so I'm allowed to go and spend it.

Assess and review (pages 20–21)

1 a) Before she knew it b) Even though she was seven
   c) After all the noise d) Now that he was in Year 6
2 a) I b) I c) S d) S
3 Answers will vary
   'What would you like to do for your birthday Terry?' Ed asked.
   'I would like to go to the cinema or try a meal at the new Polish restaurant,' replied Terry.
   'That sounds great; I want to try there too. I will book a table for 9 p.m. on Friday,' said Ed.
4 Answers will vary
   Anthony: What were you doing in the playground?
   Blerti: We weren't doing anything, just standing around. Where were you Anthony?
   Anthony: I looked in the PE cupboard but there weren't any footballs.
5 a) do not b) would have c) will not d) did not e) should not

Word classes (pages 22–23)

1 a) *Faye's:* PN *heart:* CM *pride:* AB *team:* CL *trophy:* CM
   b) *Baljit:* PN *stress:* AB *train:* CM *Birmingham:* PN *family:* CL
2 a) They b) She c) He d) They
3 a) outside b) Before c) on d) between

Subject, object, verb and articles (pages 24–25)

1 a) benches b) sofa c) windows d) field e) pizza
2

Sentence	Subject	Object	Verb
The boy ran through the forest.	boy	forest	ran
The birds flew over the houses.	birds	houses	flew
The seeds were planted by the man.	seeds	man	planted / were planted
Louisa phoned her Mum after tea.	Louisa	Mum	phoned

CUT HERE

3 a / the, the, an, an

4 **a)** bright green car **b)** Siamese kitten **c)** Year 6 girls **d)** house plant

Using the active and passive voice (pages 26–27)

1 **a)** A **b)** P **c)** A **d)** P **e)** P **f)** P **g)** A **h)** A

2 **a)** The boy band sang the winning song.
b) Grandma baked the delicious apple pie.
c) The emergency services swiftly answered the phone call.
d) The teenage girl drove the stolen car.

3 **a)** The nest was built carefully by the bird.
b) The world motor racing record was beaten by the blue team.
c) The book was ripped in half by the toddler.
d) The literacy books were marked by the teacher.

Comparative and superlative (page 28)

1

Adjective	Comparative	Superlative
happy	happier	happiest
good	better	best
big	bigger	biggest
bad	worse	worst
little	less	least
busy	busier	busiest
many	more	most
narrow	narrower	narrowest

Identifying expanded noun phrases (page 29)

1 **a)** I saw the old green car or old green car near the house.
b) She was wearing a bright green dress.
c) The cute Siamese kitten or cute Siamese kitten sat near the tree.
d) I bought a wooden table with a glass top.
e) Her garden was full of blooming, beautiful flowers.

2 Answers will vary
a) her noisy group of friends in the distance.
b) old cobbled wall near the stream.

Using question tags (page 30)

1 **a)** didn't you **b)** hasn't he **c)** don't you **d)** hasn't she

2 **a)** can't we **b)** won't he **c)** isn't it **d)** won't I **e)** wasn't it
f) shouldn't we **g)** isn't it **h)** didn't they

Identifying verb phrases and prepositional phrases (page 31)

1 **a)** had played **b)** were swimming **c)** had been reading **d)** were crying
2 **a)** at the foot of the stairs **b)** into the room **c)** in the tin
d) from my parents **e)** in the weedy, overgrown garden
f) under the soft blanket

Joining sentences in various ways (pages 32–33)

1 Answers will vary
a) The bus driver beeped his horn and I did likewise.
b) Unfortunately the new chairs were not delivered on time so we have to sit on the floor!

2 **a)** until **b)** because

3 **a)** Mum made a cake although she was feeling tired. / Although she was feeling tired, Mum made a cake.
b) Jamie threw a chair; therefore at school he got a detention.
c) Ben was confused by the game whereas Tim understood how to play it. / Whereas Ben was confused by the game, Tim understood how to play it.
d) There are many different fruits, such as: apples, oranges and pears.

Conjunctions and connectives (pages 34–35)

1 **a)** but / before **b)** and / when / so **c)** so / but / although

2 **a)** although **b)** and

3 **a)** he had finished playing football. ✓ **b)** she had originally forgotten her ticket. ✓
c) she had not been invited. ✓ **d)** he scores this penalty. ✓

Using the colon accurately (pages 36–37)

1 Answers will vary
a) cars, shoppers, children and irate drivers!
b) full of angry faces, beeping horns and a sense of chaos!

2

The bike was very popular:	she worked carefully and completed all of her work on time.
The ice-cream sundae was amazing:	some days it is sunny and other days it rains.
Pritika tried her best every day:	it had five gears and enhanced steering.
The weather in England varies:	decorated with chocolate sprinkles, wafers and raspberry sauce.

3 Answers will vary
a) a car for little Jimmy, a radio for Grandpa, new slippers for Mum and a bone for Lucky!
b) Amy worked in the garden all day
c) daily baths, plenty of feeds and lots of cuddles of course.
d) Tom was keen on sport

Punctuation of bullet points (page 38)

1 **a)** Before you cross the road, remember to:
 • look left;
 • look right;
 • look left again;
 • cross the road safely.
b) Every time you do a piece of work you should:
 • Write the title.
 • Write the date.
 • Underline your headings.

How hyphens can be used (page 39)

1 Answers will vary
a) looks young **b)** mean with money **c)** bad tempered **d)** one after the other
e) full of action

2 Answers will vary
a) The dentist recommended that Emma should drink sugar-free juice to improve the condition of her teeth.
b) Stephen had a reputation for being accident-prone: he had broken his leg five times in two years!

Using a semicolon (page 40)

1 **a)** the stars are out. **b)** a dark figure appeared. **d)** you may get dehydrated.

2 Answers will vary
a) her favourite show was 'The Wizard of Oz'.
b) the children were not enjoying their holidays.
c) everybody rushed there for the Grand Opening.
d) football is very popular amongst Year 6 boys.

Changing verbs into nouns (page 41)

1 **a)** apology, tourist, dancer, reduction, operation, happiness, concentration, education, teacher, location, satisfaction, demonstration, information, decision

Recap of word classes (pages 42–43)

1 **a)** noun ✓ **b)** article ✓ **c)** adjective ✓ **d)** noun ✓ **e)** connective ✓
f) noun ✓ **g)** pronoun ✓ **h)** adverb ✓

Assess and review (pages 44–46)

1 **a)** formal, active **b)** formal, passive **c)** formal, active **d)** informal, active

2 **a)** shorter **b)** taller / bigger **c)** richest / wealthiest **d)** greediest
e) shorter / smaller **f)** kinder / nicer / friendlier **g)** brighter / lighter

3 **a)** didn't he? **b)** won't she? **c)** isn't it?

4 **a)** The council collected the bins on Wednesday. **b)** The police directed the traffic. **c)** Mrs Smith bought the car. **d)** The children ate the pizza.

5 Answers will vary
a) the old barren tree that overlooked the cottage
b) the black dwarf rabbit crouching under the wooden bench
c) the old-fashioned teacher standing behind the desk
d) the colourful jester hat perched on the hat stand
e) the red tourist bus that stopped near Buckingham Palace